A
Family Heirloom Book

" Father
was
Quite a Boy "

As Written by Father

— With a little help from

"Thought Starters" and "Memory Jogs"

by Harry and Gloria McMahan

"Every family should write its own history!"

— This was the point made by Margaret Mead, the famous anthropologist and author, at the special three-day program, "Kin and Communities" sponsored by the Smithsonian Institution.

These special "Family Heirloom" books were inspired by the idea. Why can't every family be encouraged to write their own history?

"Grandfather Was Quite a Boy " and "Grandma Was Quite a Girl" were the first two in this "Family Heirloom" series. Now the family moves on . . .

So here are the "thought starters" and "memory jogs" to get to go back in his memory and write down that history, along with his own experiences. (There's another book for Mother, too.)

So, Dad, it's all yours! Tell us all about it! What was the world like . . . through your eyes . . . as you were growing up . . .

McMahan
Box 1537
Escondido, Calif. 92025

Dedicated to...

John William McMahan, general practitioner and surgeon. He was credited with bringing more than 2,500 babies into this world . . .and never lost a Mother! He was an expert fisherman, hunter, chess player, artist and sometimes poet and a very special Father to the six boys he McMahan'd . . . including Harry . . .

INDEX

INDEX CONTINUED . . .

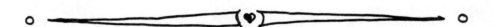

What is A Father?

Fathers have been around ever since that apple was plucked in the Garden of Eden.

And a lot of apple cores have been tossed around since. Eve always admits that this man might be very essential to the business of making her a Mother.

But the whole business of being a family gets tied into knots and ribbons and emotions as we look up our family trees and realize that so much of where we're going is dependent on where we've been.

Father is the dominant figure with the tree's trunk and branches to carry Life to Eve's leaves and to the fruit of the tree. Even in a world of changing cultures and customs, the traditions stretch like rubber bands but more often: they snap back to a band of gold. Love and pride and responsibility and all the other magic ingredients just haven't changed that much.

Father has to be a patient man, waiting for the family to start showing up, but then he is building and shaping the dreams and realities that welcome the new one into this midst.

Make him a toy. Make her a crib. Make a heart welcome. Of course, ol' Dad does have a few other functions on his way to being a Grandfather and it's a wandering path of exploration that all the psychologists and psychiatrists and anthropologists can never fully explain.

It is the traveling of the path itself that makes Life so very interesting, so very personal. Meander the path if you will. Separate the good times from the tough times. It is the Tree of Life, Dad— and you have planted it . . .

HWM

Family Photos

INSERT DAD'S FAVORITE PHOTO

(AND THEN HE WRITES:)

Today, the day I am writing this for you, is _____

_____and I am _____years old.

I have lived a good life and now I want to tell my family all about it.

To begin at the beginning, I was born in

_____ , on_____

in the year _____

My parents officially named me_____

but most of the time they just called me

_____

As a matter of vital information, I weighed into this world at

_____ pounds and _____ ounces.

Stark naked, that is . . .

_____

_____

_____

_____

_____

_____

_____

_____

_____

DAD'S SCRAPBOOK

A good time is like life insurance. The older you get the more it costs.

I Remember My Mother:

Mother was then _____ years old and My Father was _____.
As a child I remember the house we lived in:

_____

_____

_____

_____

_____

_____

And I remember a few of the nicknames the family and

friends gave me as I grew up: _____

_____

And the first chores I had to do: _____

_____

_____

_____

_____

_____

ARTEMUS WARD said it:

"I intend to live within my means, even if I have to borrow money
to do it . . . "

13

FAMILY PHOTOS

My Own GRANDPARENTS.
— And how I remember them:
(Including a few things I've heard!)

Mother's Folks: _____

_____

_____

_____

_____

_____

_____

Dad's Folks: _____

_____

_____

_____

_____

_____

 **AN OLD EPITAPH (CARVED IN 1579).**

Here is my wife
  And please let her lie —
Now she's at rest
  And so am I . . .

15

When I was growing up, a boy would be "good" for a quarter.
Nowadays, a new generation is more apt to be good for nothing.

16

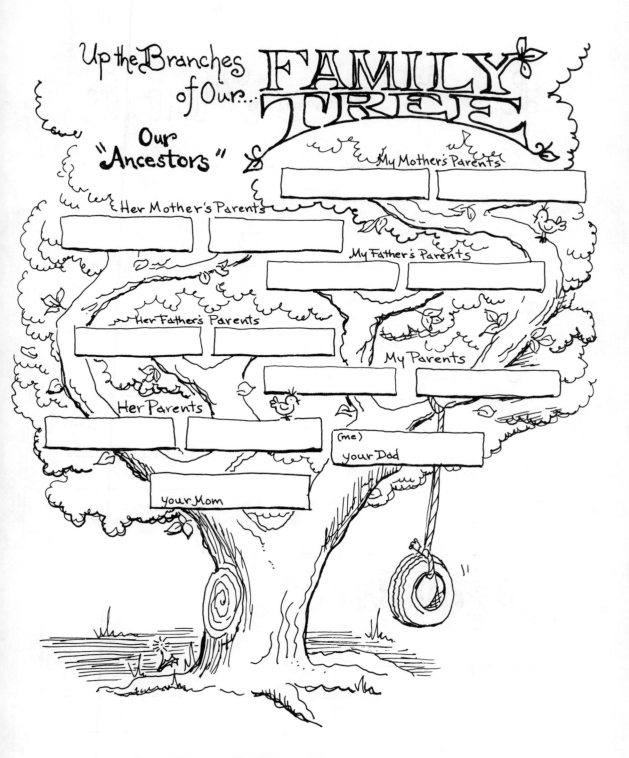

Up the Branches of Our... FAMILY TREE

Our "Ancestors"

My Mother's Parents

Her Mother's Parents

My Father's Parents

Her Father's Parents

My Parents

Her Parents

(me) your Dad

your Mom

A Lot of Interesting People Went Before You!
And I hope you add some nice twigs after me!

Little Things about my Aunts

_____

_____

_____

_____

_____

my UNCLEs

_____

_____

_____

_____

_____

And COUSINs

_____

_____

_____

_____

_____

FIRST
"FIRST MEMORIES"

My First — My *Very First* — Thing Remembered: _____

_____

My First Day in School: _____

_____

_____

The Games We Played: _____

_____

_____

My First "Paddling" — and Why! _____

_____

My First Injury: _____

_____

_____

_____

My Nicest Neighbor: _____

_____

My Favorite Teacher: _____

_____

My First "Club": _____

_____

"Reflections on Life"

Don't count your chickens before you hear from the rooster.;

When you're wrong, no one forgets. And when you're right, no one remembers.

Modern science has created everything
in the modern kitchen you could want —
except a woman who will stay in it . . .

I can't always tell whether that mechanic is working on my car — or on me.

We know a Boy Scout who always did his "Good Deed" the first thing
in the morning — and got it over with . . .

Never marry a woman who has so much will power she can walk past a
mirror without looking in it.

Why is it a small mind always seems to go with a big mouth . . . ?

OSCAR WILDE said it: "A man cannot be too careful in his choice
of enemies."

You say you have no secrets from your wife? You mean . . .
no secrets? Or no wife?

Inside every fat man, there's a thin man trying to keep
his clothes altered.

You: Who's Who

Outside of our immediate family, we have some famous — and wonderful — friends and relatives, like: _____

_____

_____

_____

_____

_____

_____

_____

_____

THINGS TO REMEMBER:

It's a wise husband who always remembers his wife's birthday.
And forgets her age . . .

_____

_____

_____

_____

_____

_____

_____

_____

_____

_____

PA'S SUNDAY WISDOM:

If you complain about Mom's Sunday dinner, please don't do it with your mouth full.

Brothers & Sisters

(Or why I wanted to be an Only Child!)

Their names and nicknames: _____

_____

_____

Where their names came from: _____

_____

_____

_____

Their Hobbies: _____

_____

_____

Their Work: _____

_____

_____

_____

BANK ON IT:

When you make something, learn to save something — so you'll
still have something when you have nothing . . .

HOUSEFUL of RELATIVES

(And What I Think of Them!)

Their Names: (Now, see the numbers on the OPPOSITE

PAGE — and see what I'd use to describe each:

_____ _____

_____ _____

_____ _____

_____ _____

_____ _____

_____ _____

_____ _____

YOU? Why I'd give *you* these numbers:

6, 12, 15, 19 (and maybe 25, too!)

ABSENT-MINDED? WHO, ME?

Now they tell me I'm getting absent-minded: It seems I took my car to the Beauty Parlor — and left my wife at the Service Station to get lubricated . . .

Adjectives for Relatives

1. crazy
2. funny
3. always laughing
4. truthful
5. courageous
6. loving
7. reliable
8. good
9. sourpuss
10. always crying
11. excitable
12. trustworthy
13. busybody
14. unreliable
15. sweet
16. honest
17. loyal
18. busy
19. dear
20. spooky
21. a kook!

or I'd say

22. I wouldn't trust him with a rusty nickel _____

23. Goofy as a giraffe with a knot in his neck _____

24. Pure as the driven snow, but she drifted _____

25. Honest as the day is long — during an eclipse _____

26. He has a mind like a bear trap — he just hasn't caught anything yet _____

ADVICE TO A SON:
Tell your Mother I said "no"
Contrari-wise, I have to guess
That is the surest way I know
To get that woman to say "yes"...

_____

_____

_____

_____

_____

_____

_____

_____

OL' ABE LINCOLN said it:

"When you have an elephant by the hind leg and he is trying to run away, it's best to let him run . . ."

You Have to START ...Sometime!

I was:

_____ months old when I started to speak . . .

_____ months old when I started to walk . . .

_____ years old when I used a hammer . . .

_____ years old when I learned to make my bed and clean my room . . .

_____ years old when I learned to make a good spit ball . . .

_____ years old when I learned to cook.

_____

_____

_____

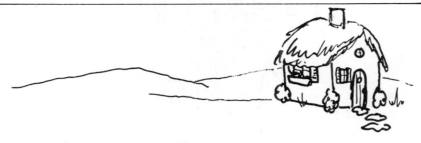

LIFE'S UPS & DOWNS

Be it a cottage, a condo, a shack —
There's always a mortgage keeps holding us back . . .

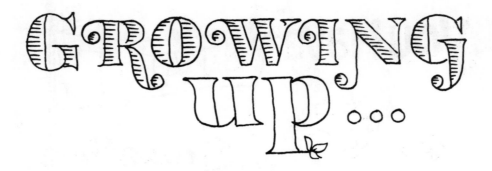

GROWING UP...

_____ When I was this many years old:

_____ I got lost away from home

_____ I first kissed a girl

_____ I smoked my first cigarette

_____ I had my first drink

_____ I had my first date

_____ I got a traffic ticket

_____ I got hauled into court

_____ I spent a night in jail

FATHER KNOWS BEST:
Keep your mouth shut and people will think you really know
what you're talking about.

ME AS A YOUNG MAN:

I suppose you could describe me as:

_____ Shy

_____ brash

_____ lean (skinny!)

_____ handsome

_____ romantic

_____ intellectual

_____ athletic

_____ adventurous

_____ bold

_____ timid

_____ fat

_____ *very* handsome!

_____ *very* romantic

_____ not smart — *shrewd!*

_____ muscle-bound

_____ poetic

_____

_____

DAD'S THINK-ABOUT-IT:
He who says he never boasts is boasting . . .

Good Times & Bad

I was in a play _____

_____

I learned to dance _____

_____

I won a contest _____

_____

I got my first pet _____

_____

I had my first "date" _____

_____

I had the measles _____

I had mumps _____

I had chickenpox _____

I had my tonsils out _____

STRICTLY MEDICINAL:

Brandy improves with age, they say. And some say that age
improves with brandy.

Things I Like to COLLECT

Friends, Of Course: _____

And Stamps _____

And Trains _____

And Coins (oh, yes!) _____

And Ties _____

And _____

_____

DAD'S 100-WATT GLOW:

Let your Light so shine that it doesn't cast shadows on your neighbor.

LOVE  HATE

___ I Love   or   I Hate ___

_____	Getting up in the morning	_____
_____	Taking a cold bath	_____
_____	Talking to strangers	_____
_____	Having to buy a new suit	_____
_____	Going to the dentist	_____
_____	Buying a new car	_____
_____	Working with an old car	_____
_____	Watching television	_____
_____	Making a speech	_____
_____	Fixing things around the house	_____
_____	Moving to a new home	_____

_____

_____

_____

_____

OVERHEARD FROM NEXT DOOR:

"If you were my husband, I'd put poison in your coffee."
  "Yeah, and if I were your husband . . . I'd take it . . ."

_____

_____

_____

_____

_____

_____

_____

_____

_____

_____

_____

_____

FATHER'S ELECTRIC OBSERVATION:

Power corrupts, they say. And you might note that the local
Power & Light company is showing quite a profit these days . . .

34

Things I've BROKEN

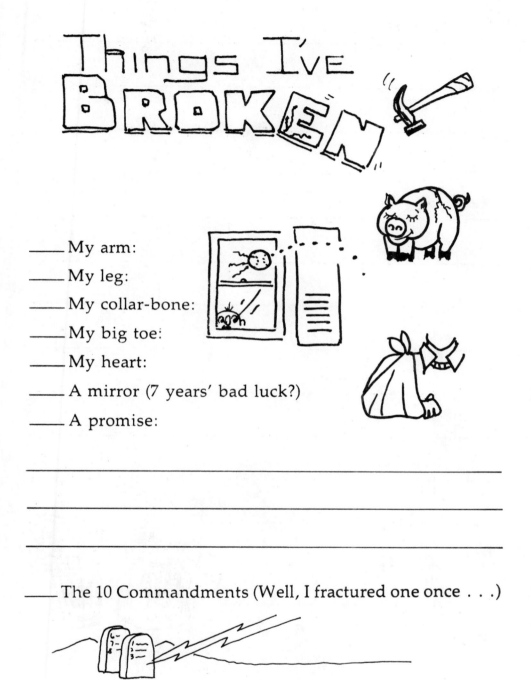

____ My arm:

____ My leg:

____ My collar-bone:

____ My big toe:

____ My heart:

____ A mirror (7 years' bad luck?)

____ A promise:

_____

_____

_____

____ The 10 Commandments (Well, I fractured one once . . .)

EPITAPH FOR AN OLD FRIEND:

Gone to join his tonsils, his adenoids and his appendix . . .

_____

_____

_____

_____

_____

_____

_____

_____

_____   _____

_____

_____

SHE RUNS A TEMPERATURE:

My wife, I think, was born a fooler
 When days are hot, she wants it cooler —
--And when it's cool, "Please make it hot!"
 She much prefers that which is not . . .

Happiness is a Woman Called My Wife ...

I met her _____

and it was (   )/wasn't (   ) love at

first sight:

Our first date_____

My favorite nickname for her was _____

And she called me _____

We were engaged_____

And married_____on _____

    in_____at _____

The best man was _____
      (really, *I* was the best man, she said...!)

Our honeymoon: _____

_____

The first place we lived_____

_____

Our first fight: _____

_____

The anniversary I remember most: _____

_____

Things I Hated Doing

(As A Child)

Making my bed —————————————————

Picking up my clothes —————————————

Putting my toys away —————————————

Keeping clean —————————————————

Taking a bath —————————————————

Wiping the dishes —————————————————

Taking a nap —————————————————

Writing "thank you" letters ——————————

Staying in on a rainy day ——————————

—————————————————————————

—————————————————————————

—————————————————————————

—————————————————————————

— See? — Things haven't changed so much for children today

— and they've got tv!

THE OLD MAN'S ADVICE TO THE LOVELORN:
The safest month in which to get married is Deseptembuary...

I PREFER

_____ small town / big city _____

_____ home cooking / restaurants _____

_____ driving / just riding _____

_____ early rising / late sleeping _____

_____ shaving myself / barber shop _____

_____ earning money / spending it _____

_____ apartment / house _____

_____ one wife / two wives _____

PAPA'S PERPLEXING PROBLEM:

How do you fall into a woman's arms — without falling into her hands . . .?

JOBS
I HAVE DONE:
POSITIONS
I HAVE HELD:

_____

_____

_____

_____

_____

_____

_____

_____

_____

_____

_____

IN THE DRIVER'S SEAT:

I can drive:

    A car _____

    A tractor _____

    A hard bargain _____

    A 10-penny nail _____

    A pair of mules _____

    A camel _____

    A dog-sled team _____

    A racing car _____

    A horse to water _____

    (But I can't make him drink)

And I can:

    Pick a lock _____ Put up preserves _____

    Figure out puzzles _____

    Work over half the cross-word puzzle _____

    Barbecue a steak _____ Mow the grass _____

    Figure out the horse races _____

    Guess people's ages _____

    Milk a cow _____ Dance a jig _____

JUST ASKING . . .

Now, I wouldn't say he is insane just because he talks to himself.
But he might be . . . if he listened . . .

PRESCRIPTIONS:

Exercise helps to kill germs. The problem is how to get the germs to exercise.

My good doctor now prescribes for me a new pill that lowers my blood pressure. Then sends me a bill that raises it right up again!

I heard this man was blind from drinking coffee. He left his spoon in the cup . . .

He charged nothing for his advice. --Possibly a little more than it was actually worth.

If you think you have amnesia, forget about it . . .

The best cure for insomnia: get lots of sleep.

Statistics show that marriage prevents suicide. And vice versa . . .

An apple a day keeps the doctor away. And an onion a day keeps everyone away.

He had trouble with his breathing —
but the doctor gave him something
that stopped that.

LIFE IS ONE PILL AFTER ANOTHER:
Baby aspirin . . . school tablets . . .prescription cold tablets . . . vitamin tablets . . . stone tablets . . .

I Do Believe. . .
I Don't Believe. . .

_____ Alcohol is America's biggest problem _____

_____ Taxes are too high for what you get _____

_____ Most automobiles wear out too fast _____

_____ Smoking is harmful to your health _____

_____ Women's Lib isn't working like it should _____

FATHER'S MOTTO OF THE WEEK:
Never put off 'til tomorrow something you can get someone else to do today.

Who's Superstitious?

Of course, I'm not superstitious, but I think it wise to use good caution when:

    a. I walk under a ladder: _____

    b. A black cat crosses my path: _____

    c. On Friday, the 13th: _____

    d. When I break a mirror: _____

    e. When I get the turkey's wishbone: _____

    f. After being married for 13 years! _____

    g. _____

And, there's a *ghost story* I believe in _____

(I should — I lived through it!) _____

_____

_____

_____

_____

_____

_____

LAW OF SUPPLIN' DE MAN:

Married men don't really live longer than single men. It just seems longer.

When I Look back I have to "CHUCKLE"

The silliest thing I ever did:

_____

_____

_____

_____

The second silliest thing I ever did:

_____

_____

_____

_____

The SMARTEST thing I ever did:

_____

_____

_____

_____

The time I almost faced death:

_____

_____

_____

_____

The time I "almost" made a fortune:

_____

_____

_____

_____

THE PENALTY FOR BIGAMY:

Two Mothers-in-Law.

The "BESTS"

The Best Vacation I ever had, growing up!:

_____

_____

The Best Year I enjoyed in school:

_____

_____

The Best car we ever owned:

_____

_____

My first "Best Sweetheart" — till I was 10:

_____

My next "Best Sweetheart" — till I was 20:

_____

My best "Best Sweetheart" since:

_____

_____

Favorites in my MEMORY

My Favorite *Color:* _____

My Favorite *Flowers:* _____

My Favorite *Aftershave:* _____

My Favorite *Day of the Year:* _____

My Favorite *Time of the Day:* _____

My Favorite *Musical Instrument:*

_____

My Favorite *Poem:* _____

_____

_____

_____

_____

_____

_____

My Favorite *Melody:* _____

_____

_____

 THE HAIRLESS TRUTH:
A class reunion always surprises you when you see how many of
the ol' boys have gone bald . . .

48

Pastimes in PAST TIMES

Kissing under the bleachers: year:

_____/_____

Roller skating:

_____/_____

Helping build a "Fort":

_____/_____

Licking the ice cream paddle:

_____/_____

Popping corn:

_____/_____

Playing with girls (ugh!?!!):

_____/_____

Flying a kite:

_____

"Skinny Dippin":

_____

Throwing snowballs:

_____

Toasting marshmallows:

_____/_____

Surprise parties:

_____/_____

FAMILY PHOTOS

50

Some of my Best Friends Before I was 10:

1. _____
   _____

2. _____
   _____

3. _____
   _____

4. _____
   _____

5. _____
   _____

6. _____
   _____

7. _____
   _____

8. _____
   _____

9. _____
   _____

10. _____
    _____

Some of my Best Friend's as a Young Man

1 _____

_____

2 _____

_____

3 _____

_____

4 _____

_____

5 _____

_____

6 _____

_____

7 _____

_____

8 _____

_____

9 _____

_____

10 _____

_____

Some of my Best Friends For Life:

1 _____

_____

2 _____

_____

3 _____

_____

4 _____

_____

5 _____

_____

6 _____

_____

7 _____

_____

8 _____

_____

9 _____

_____

10 _____

_____

_____

_____

_____

_____

_____

_____

_____

_____

E. H. RICHARDS said it:

A wise old owl sat in an oak
  The more he said, the less he spoke —
The less he spoke, the more he heard . . .
Why aren't we like that wise old bird?

I Guess I've Known a Few "Odd Balls"

The Craziest Kid I had as a Playmate:

_____

The Nuttiest Girl in School:

_____

The Funniest Joker I ever Met:

_____

The Kookiest Gal I ever Met:

_____

The Worst Teacher I ever knew:

_____

The Meanest Man in Town:

_____

The Most Memorable Person I ever Met:

_____

- And the One Person Who Most Influenced My Life:

_____

MY FAVORITE

My favorite saying always has been: _____

_____

_____

_____

My favorite person — outside the family:

_____

My favorite pet of my lifetime: _____

_____

And some other pets I well remember:

_____

_____

My favorite hobby: _____

_____

_____

_____

Some of the FIRST LOVES of my Life

Fire Trucks & Trains _____

Teddy Bear _____

Rocking Horse _____

Marbles _____

Building blocks _____

Crossing My Eyes _____

Baseball Glove _____

Drawing Pictures _____

Collecting _____

The Fir$t

The first money I ever earned — *really* earned: _____

_____

_____

_____

The first paycheck job I ever held: _____

_____

_____

_____

The first time I bought something *"big"* with my own money:

_____

_____

_____

2"
JAW
BREAKERS
25¢

_____

_____

THREE KINDS OF MEN:
There are three kinds of men who fail to understand women:
1. Young men.
2. Middle-aged men.
3. Old men.

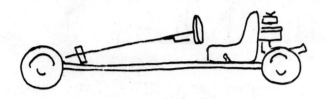

The first time I drove — the first car I remember: _____

_____

_____

_____

The first time I paid the rent: _____

_____

_____

_____

The most important purchase I ever made: _____

_____

_____

_____

_____

_____

HISTORICAL NOTE:

Rome wasn't built in a day. --Sounds like one of those government projects . . .

FAMILY PHOTOS

I Wore a Lot of Clothes~

In my lifetime I estimate I have owned:

—— pair of sox

—— pair of shorts

—— pair of shoes

—— suits and pants

—— shirts

—— handkerchiefs

—— ties

I Ate a Lot of Food~

—— dozen eggs

—— gallons of milk

—— slices of bread

—— pieces of pie

—— cups of coffee

_____

_____

(— I guess I was pretty hungry!)

I KNOW A GUY:

His feet are so big he sometimes puts his trousers on over his head.

ABC FOR DAD

A   is for Adam and the Ages of Man,
     B is for Boy, growing fast as he can.

C's for the Children who grow with the lad
     D is for Dogs — for the kids and for Dad.

E   is the Epitaph (Life's helping to write)
     F is the Flowers (for Mom for tonight).

G   is the Grandpa Dad some day will be
     H is the Home to raise your family.

I's an Idea that burns in your mind —
     And J is the Joy that a king wouldn't find.

L   is Life's Laughter, the fun and the jokes
     M's Merry Christmas, back home with the folks.

N   is for Nice Times and the New Year that came
     O is for Old Friends, forever the same.

P   is for "Papa!" — you're glad you're a Pop —
     The Q is for Questions — and kids never stop.

R   is the Remedy you seek for life's woe
     And S is the Spirit that keeps on the go . . .

T   is for Time — Father's Time for his cheers:
     He's Unique, Underrated for all of his years.

We give Xtra honors, You've lived Life with a Zest —
     And the next generation will have memories — the best!

SO MANY THINGS TO REMEMBER

— The First Time I ever gambled —

_____

_____

_____

—The First Time I ever went fishing — (and caught a fish *this*

big!) _____

_____

_____

— The First Time I was angry enough to hit someone —

_____

_____

_____

— The First Time I sold something —

_____

_____

_____

— The First Time I fell in love —

_____

_____

_____

MY FAVORITE SPORTS STARS

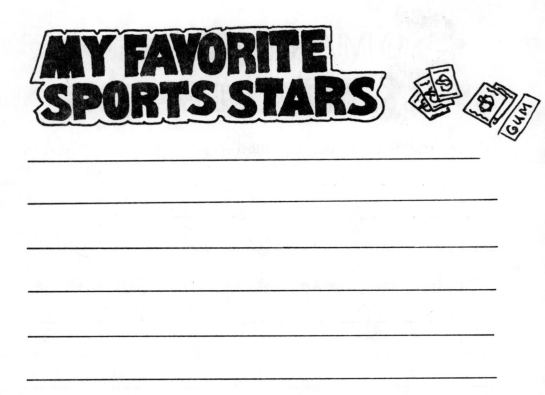

_____

_____

_____

_____

_____

THE GREATEST SPORTS EVENT I EVER SAW:

_____

_____

_____

_____

They say he lived to be 93 — and didn't have an enemy in the world.
He'd outlived 'em all!

My Favorite Games + Sports

(Marked: "1-2-3" as I like 'em)

____ Tennis

____ Swimming

____ Horseback Riding

____ Football

____ Baseball

____ Horse shoes

____ Horse Racing (& Betting!)

____ Fishing

____ Hunting

____ Tiddle-de-Winks

____ Ping-Pong

— And the nearest I ever came to being a Sport Champ —

_____

_____

_____

ONE MAN REFLECTS:

The latest census lists 35,000 different types of occupations.
Then how come my cousin can't get a job?

_____

_____

_____

_____

_____

_____

_____

_____

_____

_____

_____

HARRY EMERSON FOSDICK said it:

Hating people is like burning down your home to get rid of a rat.

66

My Auto Biography

(Family Cars I Remember Well)

Ford	Cougar	Pontiac
BMW	Bobcat	Volvo
Chevy	Mercedes-Benz	Fiat
Buick	Mustang	Renault
VW	Pinto	Simca
Toyota	Maverick	Saab
Model T	Cricket	Marmon
Opel	T-Bird	Honda
De Lorean	Colt	Nash
Oldsmobile	Impala	Hudson
Rolls-Royce	Road Runner	Jaguar
Dodge	Ram	DeSoto
Imperial	Subaru	Chrysler
Jeep	Packard	Pierce-Arrow
Edsel	Citroen	Rambler
	Plymuth	*Lexus*
		Jaguar
		Cad
		Lincoln
		Lincoln Zepher

And My Own First "Wheels":

Scooter _____

Roller Skates _____

Bicycle _____

Red wagon _____

Soap-box _____

Tricycle _____

_____   _____

_____

_____

_____

_____

_____

_____

_____

_____

_____

_____

_____

_____

_____

MORNING REFLECTIONS:

Early to bed, early to wake . . .
Remind me to pass up that devil's food cake!

EVERYTHING "HAPPENS" TO ME...

(Well, some of these Things, at Least. . .)

I was in an accident: _____

_____

I was in an earthquake: _Denver Colorado_____

_____

I was in a fire: _____

_____

I was in a tornado: _____

_____

I was in a fight: _____

_____

I was robbed: _at gun point on old Route 66_
in Tucumcari New Mexico

I was caught naked: _____

_____

But, ONE TIME, I was a hero

_____

_____

THE 11th COMMANDMENT:
Thou shalt not fold, spindle or mutilate.

The Happiest Christmas that I Remember

As a Child:

_____

_____

As a Young Man:

_____

_____

In My Teens:

_____

_____

After I Married:

_____

_____

After my Children Were Born:

_____

_____

— But, there was *ONE* Christmas I'd Rather Forget:

_____

_____

_____

HAPPY HOLIDAYS

My most romantic New Year's Eve:

_____

_____

My noisiest Fourth of July:

_____

_____

My most exciting Valentine's Day:

_____

_____

My happiest Birthday:

_____

_____

My craziest Halloween:

_____

_____

My gladdest Thanksgiving:

_____

_____

_____

_____

HOLIDAY OBSERVATION:

Best recipe for a good cook: Stir in a happy family, home for the holidays.

_____

_____

_____

_____

_____

_____

_____

_____

_____

Some Funny Things :

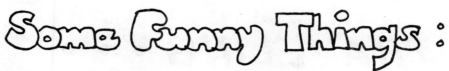

The funniest joke anyone ever played on me:

_____

_____

The funniest joke I ever played on someone else:

_____

_____

_____

— And my most embarrassing moment:

_____

_____

_____

_____

The funniest thing that happened on my honeymoon:

_____

_____

The funniest thing that happened at school:

_____

_____

_____

_____

The funniest thing that ever happened at home:

_____

_____

TRAVELING • • •

The first trip I remember:

_____

_____

The first train ride I remember:

_____

_____

The first airplane trip I remember:

1936 in an open cockpit airplane

Grand Rapids, Michigan. My 8th birthday

My favorite city when I was young:

_____

_____

My favorite hotel:

_____

_____

Some cities I would still like to visit:

_____

_____

_____

YOUNG DREAMS:
She dressed in silks (my satisfaction!)
Her movements were pure liquefaction . . .

74

The U.S.A.

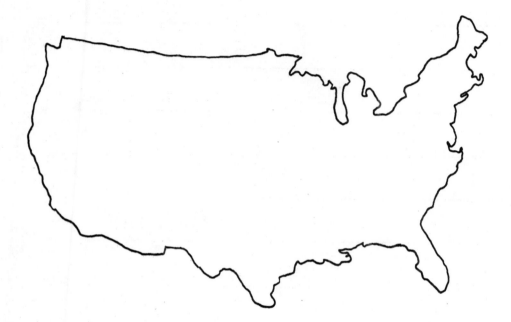

Places I've Visited

Every state in The U.S.

75

_____

_____

_____

_____

_____

_____

_____

_____

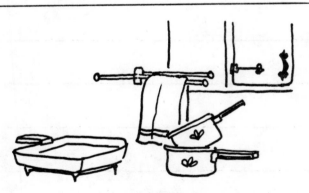

ASK DAD:

The honeymoon is over when he stops helping with the dishes.
And has to start doing them all by himself.

Women are WONDERFUL

Except . . .

____ when they tell you how to drive . . .

____ when they try to hammer a nail . . .

____ when they try to explain where they've been . . .

____ when they try to build a campfire . . .

____ when they try to judge a likely son-in-law . . .

I think the 3 most interesting women in history were:

Eve _____

Cleopatra _____

Helen of Troy _____

Mata Hari _____

Queen Victoria _____

Jackie Kennedy _____

Marilyn Monroe _____

Greta Garbo _____

Marlene Dietrich _____

Shirley MacLaine _____

Diana Ross _____

Brooke Shields _____

_____ Signed

_____
Male Chauvinist

MORE LĬKES & DĬSLĬKES

My favorite singer:

_____

_____

My favorite newspaper:

_____

_____

My favorite TV star:

_____

_____

The best movie I ever saw:

_____

_____

My favorite movie star:

_____

My favorite romantic novel:

_____

The *worst* movie star of all:

_____

OVER THE BACK FENCE:
You can forgive almost anything in a friend — except, maybe, too much success.

The "EST" Things

The sickest I ever got:

_____

The maddest I ever got:

_____

The tiredest I ever got:

_____

The most jealous I ever got:

_____

The smartest trick I ever pulled:

_____

The biggest mistake I made in my life:

_____

The luckiest I ever was:

_____

The proudest I ever was:

_____

_____

PARENTAL PROVERBS:
Nothing is often the cleverest thing you can say.

PAPA'S POP CORN

At 7 he was all ears —
At 17 all smiles —
At 47 all paunch —
And at 77, all in . . .

A man's ego is about the only thing that keeps growing just with its own fertilizer.

BUYING A NEW CAR?

I'm intrigued with the way they name cars: Mustang, Jaguar, Ram, Impala. And for the birds: Falcon, Hawk, the Eagle. --It's interesting, though, no matter which one I buy I wind up with a Turkey.

You can tell a great deal about a woman
when you find out what she laughs at . . .

Intuition is a woman's label for plain, ordinary suspicion.

He reads very little. Says he's afraid he'll wear out his new glasses.

There may be little difference between monogamy and bigamy. Each may be a case of one wife too many.

WILL ROGERS said it: "The income tax has made more liars out of American people than golf has . . . "

He makes what he calls a Mona Lisa
cocktail. After a couple, his girl
can't get that silly grin off her face . . .

Man is the only animal that needs a lawyer.

HOW'S THAT AGAIN?
Housework? My wife likes to do nothing better . . .

We do not stop laughing because we grow old. We grow old because we stop laughing,

Foods I Like or Dislike
yes ✓   NO ✓

—— artichoke ——
—— apple pie ——
—— tamales ——
—— kidney pie ——
—— eggs ——
—— liver ——
—— boiled cabbage ——
—— ice cream ——

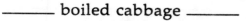

—————————————————

—————————————————

—— spinach ——
—— watermelon ——
—— steak ——
—— broccoli ——
—— mush ——
—— squash ——
—— pigsfeet ——
—— snails ——
—— lettuce ——

—————————————————

—————————————————

FAMILY Recipe FAVORITES

DON'T SAY DIET!
It is the sort of diet, I discovered, that somehow
keeps your mind on your stomach.

82

More about Food AND Cookin'

My favorite food as a child: _____

_____

My favorite as a boy: _____

_____

My life-time favorite: _____

_____

My favorite restaurant: _____

_____

One of the best meals I ever ate — anywhere:

_____

The first food I learned to cook myself: _____

_____

My favorite recipe to pass along:

_____

_____

_____

_____

_____

_____

_____

_____

_____

_____

_____

_____

_____

_____

_____

_____

THE WEIGHT WAIT:

A woman's weight is wait-and-see —
Wait — see if she can't change it.
She'll put some on — or take it off —
Or, somehow, rearrange it . . .

84

MY OWN OPINIONS !!!

Peace will never come until: ———————————————

————————————————————————————————

The trouble with airplanes: ————————————————

————————————————————————————————

Swimming in the nude: ——————————————————

————————————————————————————————

How to solve the world's overpopulation problems:

————————————————————————————————

————————————————————————————————

Man was never intended to have only *one* woman:

————————————————————————————————

————————————————————————————————

————————————————————————————————

————————————————————————————————

————————————————————————

WHERE'D YOU GET THE BLACK EYE?

Most men survive a broken leg with truth and honesty. --But a
black eye brings out the liar in the best of 'em.

_____

_____

_____

_____

_____

_____

_____

_____

_____

_____

_____

A FRIEND OF MINE:

He was a pretty smart onion in his day. But I'm afraid he's gone to seed . . .

IF—

If I had it all to do over, I'd like to:

— Be born twins, because: _____

_____

_____

— Be born in a family with ____ brothers and ____

sisters.

— Be born in a small town like _____

_____

— With a new name of my own, like _____

_____

— And grow up to have a special work: _____

_____

_____

— And get married ____ times

— And have ____ children!

— Or, maybe, really . . .

I wouldn't change a thing!

PERSISTENCE PAYS:

The woodpecker is quite a persistent salesman. He keeps knocking and, sooner or later, a worm comes to the door . . .

My Greatest Ambition . . .

As a Little boy: _____

_____

_____

_____

In My Teens: _____

_____

_____

_____

Before I got carried away in Marriage: _____

_____

_____

_____

After I married: _____

_____

_____

And Still: _____

_____

_____

_____

I Wish, I Wish, I Wish—

I Wish I Had:

____ Studied other languages,
especially _____

____ Kept my Indian penny collection

____ Kept some of the clothes I wore

____ Kept a real diary, all the years
of my life

____ Kept more pictures of the people
and places I knew

____ Asked my Mother and Father more
questions about *their* lives

____ And I wish I could talk to *one*
particular person _____

. . . just *one* more time . . .

I REALLY WISH —

It would be kinda nice to grow old enough to prove to today's
youngsters that I was right when I warned 'em how they'd turn
out.

IT WAS QUITE A CENTURY TO LIVE IN

The 20th Century Had Both Good and Bad,

But the Great Things Were Really Great:

Let me tell you what I know about . . .

The War Years _____

_____

_____

The Coming of Space Flights —

_____

My Favorite Years Were:

_____

_____

The "Rock 'n Roll" Era!

_____

_____

The fast-moving 'Sixties & 'Seventies:

_____

_____

I Lived In a World of New Inventions

(And What I Liked About Each)

Computers —

_____

Air Travel —

_____

Vitamins —

_____

Plastics —

_____

Air-Conditioning —

_____

New Kinds of Cars —

_____

_____

_____

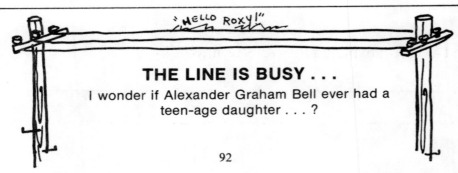

"HELLO ROXY!"

THE LINE IS BUSY . . .
I wonder if Alexander Graham Bell ever had a
teen-age daughter . . . ?

more INVENTIONS

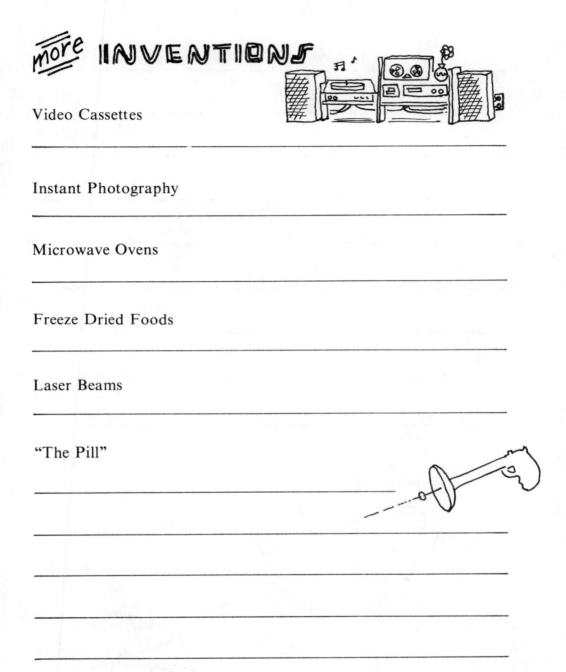

Video Cassettes

_____

Instant Photography

_____

Microwave Ovens

_____

Freeze Dried Foods

_____

Laser Beams

_____

"The Pill"

_____

_____

_____

_____

THE WORD FROM OL' DAD:
Women live longer than men. --Especially widows . . .

_____

_____

_____

_____

_____

_____

_____

_____

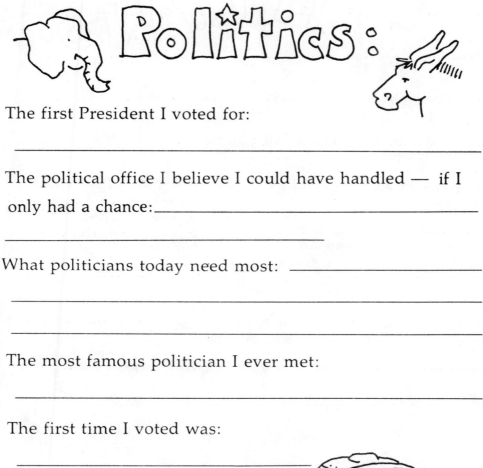

Politics:

The first President I voted for:

_____

The political office I believe I could have handled — if I

only had a chance:_____

_____

What politicians today need most: _____

_____

_____

The most famous politician I ever met:

_____

The first time I voted was:

_____

_____

The political party I believe in: _____

_____

POLITICAL POOP:

Politicians have a great deal of the cowboy in them: They
straddle the issues. They kick up a lot of dust. Then they start
throwing the bull.

POLITICIANS

Some politicians spend half their time making laws — and the other half helping their friends evade them.

Honesty is the best policy. But after the election some politicians just let the policy lapse.

A politician should be loved for the enemies he makes. Politics makes strange bad fallows.

Cheap politicians can be a most costly drain on taxpayers.

A politician soons learns the difference between "the right thing to so" and "doing the right thing."

It seems a politician is always trying to get some big investigation started And some other little investigation stopped.

Why do they call it public debt when the private taxpayer has to pay it?

Who called them "cheap politicians?" --Cheap they aren't . . .

The Senator appears to travel by hot air balloon.

The country might be better off if someone figured a way to increase the number of ex-Senators and ex-Congressmen.

The politician was truly a self-made man. -- A product of unskilled labor.

When they asked the political candidate if he was "indecisive," he answered, "Well, yes and no . . . "

Never forget that government of the people, by the people and for the people must be operated from taxes on the people . . .

Beware the politician who is too cowardly to fight and too fat to run.

The politician had a very straightforward way of dodging an issue.

He approached every question with an open mouth.

Next, to get votes, they'll vote to lower the Age of Puberty . . .

Things to Come

And I'd Like to Live Long Enough to See! .....

1. A cure for cancer

_____

2. Safer cars

_____

3. Abolition of poverty

_____

4. Peace (for more than one-half of my years

there has been a War on — somewhere!)

5. _____

6. _____

7. _____

8. _____

SOMEONE ONCE SAID:
To be ignorant of one's own ignorance is the malady of the
ignorant.

_____

_____

_____

_____

_____

_____

_____

_____

_____

_____

DAD'S PRIVATE PHILOSOPHY:

Ever notice the sunset often is brighter than the sunrise? --
That's a special promise! Tomorrow's going to be a lot better . . . .

What I Feel about PEOPLE IN GENERAL

Rich people: _____
_____

Poor People: _____
_____

People Who Gossip: _____
_____

Fat People: _____
_____

Skinny People: _____
_____

People Who Talk Too Much: _____
_____

People Too Dumb: _____
_____

People Too Book Smart: _____
_____
_____
_____

MY CHILDREN'S PHOTOS

My Father's Favorite Family Stories

_____

_____

_____

_____

_____

_____

_____

_____

_____

_____

_____

_____

_____

_____

_____

_____

_____

My Mother's Favorite Family Stories

MY BEST ADVICE
to My
♥ CHILDREN and their CHILDREN ♥

_____

_____

_____

_____

_____

_____

_____

_____

_____

_____

_____

Dad's suggestion Box

The "One" Time In My Life I'd Most Like to Live Over:

_____

_____

_____

_____

_____

_____

_____

_____

_____

The FUTURE

The Great Opportunities I see For Today's Youth in Careers and Interesting Jobs That Didn't Exist When I Was Young:

Electronics _____

Aviation _____

Space Travel _____

Plastics _____

Undersea Exploration _____

Diplomatic Fields _____

Civic Administration _____

Welfare Work _____

Peace Corps _____

Other: _____

_____

_____

_____

_____

_____

_____

_____

_____

_____

DAD'S CLEAN LOOK AT THE WORLD:

A bathtub in a boarding house has seen it all. . .

Good Deeds

The 3 nicest good deeds others have done for me:

_____

_____

_____

_____

And the 3 nicest I have tried to do for others:

_____

_____

_____

_____

HORACE MANN said it:

Lost, yesterday, somewhere between Sunrise and Sunset, two golden hours — each set with sixty diamond minutes. No reward offered . . . for they are gone forever . . ."

FATHER'S FINAL FOOTNOTES:

Fortune smiles on some. On others, she just laughs out loud.

SPEAK UP! COMPLAIN!

JOSH BILLINGS said it, a century ago: "The wheel that squeaks the loudest is the one that gets the grease . . . "

The meek will inherit the earth . . . as though they don't have enough other problems . . .

The real problem with money is that you can't use it more than once . . .

You can tell a lot about a man by noting where his dog sleeps.

"ANTHONY ADVERSE" said it: "Grow up as soon as you can. It pays. The only time you really live fully is from thirty to sixty . . . "

There is no fool like an old fool. (You just can't beat experience!)

If God really meant for us to rest on Sunday, why did he create crabgrass?

If he were twice as smart as he tries to be, he wouldn't be half as smart as he thinks he is.

Humor is food's salt and pepper that we sprinkle on conversation.

ON FLYING HIGH:

Clip a wing, a bird can't fly —
The lack of balance tells you why.
And Man, without a Woman nigh,
May lose the dream we meant to try . . .

108

My Next-to-Last...

More important than money are some of the things I give to my Children — and my Children's Children:

I give LOVE (a life-time full of it — love that you give generously and you earn full measure of, in return)

I give HAPPY MEMORIES (for these are the woven fabrics of our lives)

I give GOOD LUCK (and always the eager hope for a lottery ticket that wins!)

And LONG LIFE and an APPRECIATION for it (even as I have found it ever so wonderful) —

(And may you remember me well . . .)

NOTES

_____

_____

_____

_____

_____

_____

_____

_____

_____